CHALLENGING THE BLACK DOG

COLOUR ME

CHALLENGING THE BLACK DOG

A CREATIVE OUTLET FOR TACKLING DEPRESSION

V.J. CAST

CHALLENGING THE BLACK DOG by VJ Cast

Offbeat Brains

PO Box 164
Russell Island
Queensland 4184
Australia

offbeatbrains.com

For information about discounts available for bulk purchases, sales promotions, fund-raising and educational or community outreach needs, please contact sales@offbeatbrains.com.

Formatting & Design © VJ Cast.
Cover design © Patrick Knowles
Logo Design © Imageffects
Front + End Illustrations © Patmai de Vera

Printed by IngramSpark

Page ii, © Olka Kostenko/Stock; pages iv-v, © Patmai de Vera/Illustration; page xi, © Jhaiella Gee/Illustration; page xv, © Olka Kostenko/Stock; page 16-17, © Olka Kostenko/Stock; page 31, © mazegenerator.net/Maze; page 46, © Olka Kostenko/Stock; page 65, © Olka Kostenko/Stock; page 78-79, © Olka Kostenko/Stock; page 97, © Olka Kostenko/Stock; page 110, © Olka Kostenko/Stock; page 111, © mazegenerator.net/Maze; page 138, © Olka Kostenko/Stock; page 139, © mazegenerator.net/Maze; page 172-173, © Olka Kostenko/Stock; page 180, © Olka Kostenko/Stock; page 206-207, © Olka Kostenko/Stock; page 211, © Olka Kostenko/Stock; pages 214-216, © Patmai de Vera/Illustration.

DISCLAIMER: This book provides content related to psychological topics. The author is not licensed as an educational consultant, physician, psychologist, or psychiatrist. The author and publisher have used their best efforts in preparing the 'Challenging The Black Dog', and the information is provided "as is." We make no warranties or representation with respect to the accuracy or completeness of the contents of the journal, and we expressly disclaim any implied warranties of merchantability or fitness for any particular purpose. Resources are provided for informational purposes only and do not constitute an endorsement of any websites or other sources. Readers should be aware that websites and phone numbers listed in this book may change.

All material in 'Challenging The Black Dog' is provided for your information only and may not be construed as medical advice or instruction and should not be used as a substitute for the medical advice of physicians or mental health professionals. The reader should regularly consult a physician or mental health professional in matters relating to their health and particularly with respect to any symptoms that may require diagnosis or medical attention. Readers who fail to consult with appropriate health authorities assume the risk of any injuries that may result.

Use of this book implies your acceptance of this disclaimer.

ISBN 978-0-6482474-0-1

For J

The most selfless person I know... your amazing empathy, boundless compassion and willingness to put up with me never ceases to amaze.

For W

My beacon during the lows and my anchor during the highs. You make it all worthwhile.

ENDORSEMENTS

Challenging the Black Dog is a resource for depression sufferers by a depression sufferer. VJ's approach provides a very specific type of compassion and understanding that's only available from lived experience, yet still manages to get across the idea of personal accountability for recovery. It is a treasure trove of ideas, strategies and bite-sized prompts which can be added to by the reader. An experimental approach is encouraged! Importantly it provides hope and will complement professional expertise.

PATRICK MCGORRY AO MD PHD FRANZCP
Professor of Youth Mental Health
Orygen, the National Centre of Excellence in Youth Mental Health & the University of Melbourne

Challenging the Black Dog is a thoughtful and creative resource for teenagers and young adults dealing with depression. With an abundance of written exercises and innovative probes, it serves as an intimate guide to self-discovery and constructive change. I strongly recommend it not only for those who are experiencing the pain of depression but for all who wish to reflect deeply with the personal factors that can bring us darkly down and those that can bring us back to renewal and light.

BRIAN R. LITTLE PH.D.
Fellow, Well-Being Institute
Cambridge University

Challenging the Black Dog is immensely creative, using humour and intentional questions to encourage personal reflection. In the busyness of life slowing down and finding positive ways to manage depression is essential. Challenging the Black Dog provides information, tips and tricks on a wide range of topics in an interactive format to encourage the reader to actively participate in their recovery and tell their own story. There's something for everyone in this book.

ASSOCIATE PROFESSOR JAMES SCOTT
Child and Youth Psychiatrist
Queensland Centre for Mental Health Research

We need to ditch the 'one size fits all' stereotype of depression and anxiety, and in her book, VJ Cast provides a creative outlet for young people to be artistic, to vent if they feel like it, or to explore their thoughts and feelings in a safe, private way.

PROFESSOR JANE BURNS
University of Sydney
Founder. Chair. Strategic Advisor
@janeburns

ENDORSEMENTS

Challenging the Black Dog reminded me of the strength I gained as I went through my depression and anxiety. Although at the time it felt impossible to have any kind of happiness, I look back now and see my depression as a blessing. I used a few techniques in this book, ones that I had to research on my own since sitting in front of psychiatrists wasn't my piece of cake. I'm also very stubborn too.

There are many old and new ones in this book that I wish I had back then to help me tame my Black Dog. They are ones that I can still use today in my everyday life. There are techniques here to help calm your 'Black Dog' and create awareness about what triggers the darkness.

Similar to training our muscles to become stronger, our minds can be trained to be strong and content. We can train our 'Black Dog,' all we need is a little bit of guidance to get there. This book is a resource that you can use as a guide to psychological well-being. It guides you see the courage and strength that you have to step into the light.

You don't have to have depression and/or anxiety to read this. It has tools that you can use in everyday life. Your life is the most unique thing you'll ever have. No one gets to live your life but you. You have the power to shape it the way you want it to be, and this book is about you. You can write in it, draw, vent, scribble random things that are important and inspire you. Treat it as your companion. It's here to help and encourage you. It's a support crew in your corner, there to use anytime, anywhere.

BELLE BROCKHOFF
Professional Snowboarder & 2x Olympian
www.bellebrockhoff.com / @bellebrockhoff

What a brilliant idea - Challenging the Black Dog is a creative resource, designed to support personal reflection and insight into the experience of depression. And why shouldn't the exploration of depression be creative, stimulating and ultimately uplifting? Challenging the Black Dog effectively takes the currently popular, designer "happiness journal" to a new level and depth, confronting the reality of living with depression in a format that can be both pleasurable and relatable.

PROFESSOR JILL BENNETT
Australian Research Council Laureate Fellow, UNSW AUSTRALIA
Director of The Big Anxiety: festival of arts + science + people
thebiganxiety.org T: @thebiganxiety

TABLE OF CONTENTS

FOREWORD

It's a pleasure to have been given the opportunity to write a note to the readers of this book. Perhaps "users of this resource" is a more accurate way of putting it, because as you flip through these pages for the first time, it's a book like any other book, bound paper between covers, and uniform with the many other as-yet-pristine copies that have come off of the press. However, unlike your childhood and school text books, you're ENCOURAGED to write in it, and make it your own. Like a childhood teddy bear, it's being worn threadbare that makes it REAL.

If you think artistically, it's a blank canvas waiting for your inspirations to bring it to life. Like St. Exupery's Little Prince, you needn't worry about what "the grown ups" will think of your snake-that-ate-an-elephant. In that spirit, my daughter Jhaiella (who is 5, and blessed to think of black dogs only as large furry things that lick you) offers a Black Dog to remind you that you are the only judge of your work that really, ultimately matters, even if your years outpace your skills by a wide margin.

If words are more your thing, it's also a blank journal waiting for your thoughts and analyses. If you're musically inclined, perhaps the doodling spaces could be filled with snippets of a melody that captures the moment. Above all, don't feel constrained to do the work rigorously according to some presumed script. You probably do that too much already as it is!

If you're a blokey bloke wondering why someone gave this to you, fix things. Take 'draw a monster' and instead weld one in your shop that you can stick in the garden where the neighbours' cats like to bury their.... parcels. Your life is your script, and a nudge this way or that should never stop you finding your own way to write it. This will be a first draft that you can keep coming back to over the years, like that bear whose whereabouts you're wondering about now.

Over the last five years that the Book of the Black Dog has been taking shape, I've watched it from the sidelines as it followed the path that many dreams follow - a moment of inspiration followed by years of perspiration, to paraphrase Thomas Edison. There were down times that led to it having to, shall we say, ferment a bit more into that finer wine, leading to frustrations that are overcome by the power of the dream, which in its most essential form was to create something that would help other people by sharing "what works" on her personal journey.

This book contains many thought-provoking exercises that are aimed at helping you think differently about "Black Dog" monster. How to keep it from biting? How to mend yourself when it does? How to sit quietly with it if you can't chase it away? When its teeth sink in, there seems to be nothing else in the world - nothing you can enjoy, nothing that will take away the pain, no one to help, and besides, do you really deserve help or hope anyway? Of course you do, you just don't see it at that particular moment. However, life is an array of moments, no one exactly like another, just like the kaleidoscopic geometric designs that have been left in black and white, for you to occupy yourself with colouring-in.

Of course, colouring-in has been the rage of late, and there are many books you can buy if those particular sets of exercises helps take you out of the dark place long enough to go to the dollar shop and find some. It's part of V's astute attention to 'what works for me' that she wasn't only colouring-in, but designing patterns to colour in, long before the therapeutic craze kicked off. That astuteness also led to her adding an 'apples and oranges' exercise to analyze the useless and harmful comparisons that you tend to make when Black Dog is biting. I was indeed flattered to find that it was in partly based on work she remembered doing with me many years ago that I'd actually forgotten about until we went through the book proofs together.

It's not just drawn from therapy that V has HAD, but therapy that she has DONE, the former being a subset of the latter - including, but far from limited to, sessions in a little brick room on a subtropical island in a large bay off the southern Coral Sea. Her success in getting this book out to you reflects the active nature of a good therapeutic process - taking things away from your sessions, processing them, but finding other things that help along the way. It's a change in mindset, and the recognition that solid goal structures have big shiny things on top of a large pile of gritty little realities along the way.

Like a Bill Bryson travel book, it's more a guided hike in a dark forest, than a trip to the mechanic to have something fixed for you. On the one hand you have to have your eye on the big, personally meaningful goal to keep it going. Yet on the other hand you have to acknowledge and accept the Legos™ of Life that you'll step on along the way - those annoying, yet essential things that may slow you down, but which may in turn help you step outside of a bad moment and reflect on ways to get around them. As Paul Simon once sang, "Hello darkness, my old friend..."

It's important in goal-setting to keep the steps along the way manageable. One idea that's been around for a couple of decades, thanks to my former supervisor Prof. Brian Little, is that of a 'meaning/manageability trade-off.' We may seek meaning through enormous projects that are highly significant to us (like writing a book), should we achieve our goals, but in the process we lose manageability by having bitten off more than we can chew. We daydream and do nothing to further the dreams, spinning our tyres in emotional mires. This can bring your monster out of its doghouse to bite.

Conversely, we may keep all things manageable, by having no big dreams. In this process, we can lose sight of meaning as it sails away over the horizon while we sit tied to our moorings in the shallows, waiting for our monster to swim slowly out from shore an climb over the gunwales. Like the lengthy process that gave rise to this book, taking things in bite-sized chunks over an extended time, rather than racing to complete it as soon as possible, balances the bits of meaning in each exercise against the unmanageability of taking it on as a whole.

And thus we 'muddle through' without getting stuck at either end of the meaning/manageability spectrum. Think about it. At a page a day, it would take over six months to get through, and that's assuming you don't make a few copies of your favorites to re-do from different perspectives!

Is six months a long time to get rid of your Black Dog monster? Perhaps. But is 14 pages over 2 weeks enough to start getting it at least to heel once in a while? You'll find out, in your own time. This is a personal project that can get you started on a new approach to your life as a whole. Make it a good habit to get into, like that bear you had to have at night when you were three.

And if you find Black Dog monster sleeping in the doghouse more often than not, then put it aside for a month, or a year, or a decade, and come back as needed. Another of Prof. Little's ideas is that of a 'restorative niche,' a place where you can go and relax and just be your natural self. Whether your niche is a park bench, a towel on a beach, or in the loo at work, you can hum a bar of Sound of Silence and sing "I've come to talk to you again." And nobody will care if you're not in tune. Especially that bear.

Dr. Travis Gee
Macleay Island
15 July 2017

COLOUR ME

INTRODUCTION

25 years.

Twenty. Five. Years.

It's still hard to admit how much of my life I've struggled with my black dog in one way or another. Admit how much I've lost because I was occupied with fighting a war inside my head. I've tried to fight it without help. I've dealt with horrid experiences with multiple healthcare professionals. I've been on medication that made things worse. I've even come close to giving up entirely a few times.

I've also fought it with help. I've been fortunate enough to have some great experiences with health care professionals. I've been on medication that made things better, or at least bearable. And I've even had good times amongst all the shit-storms of bad days.

I've even come to accept that while my black dog might never go away entirely, it can at least be tamed.

But what I can't accept is another generation following behind me when they could otherwise be spared some of the intense mental pain and isolation of failing to find help early enough to make a difference to the trajectory of their life.

In fact, it's the whole reason behind the creation of Challenging the Black Dog.

I'll always strongly advocate professional treatment to give yourself the necessary tools to beat back your black dog. However, I also realise this isn't possible for many people and for a lot of different reasons.

So, while Challenging the Black Dog wasn't created to replace professional medical help, it does exist to provide a road-map to those who are lost and seeking guidance. It should, ultimately, work hand-in-hand with whatever ways you chose to seek help in fighting your mental monsters.

I've used this journal to bring together a collection of therapy types, all known to help alleviate depression, ranging from cognitive behavioural therapy (CBT) exercises to art therapy practices. Each exercise prompt is something I've personally benefited from at one point or another.

Some may work better for you than others, which has nothing to do with doing something 'wrong'! Rather it's a simple fact that everyone suffers from depression in their unique way, even if their symptoms may be similar. Correspondingly they will respond to different treatments/therapies in different ways. Something doesn't seem to be working for you? Skip it. Something works well? Grab a blank journal and repeat the exercise however many times you need.

Simply put, this journal is about pro-actively taking control of your mental well-being, and while there's no right or wrong way to use it, there's one rule you must follow: HONESTY. If you can't be honest within the safe space of your journal you can neither authentically explore yourself and your depression, nor transform yourself into an active participant in your self-care.

If what's holding you back from being truly honest is the fear someone might read your journal, hide it. The internet is a treasure trove of genuinely inventive ways for hiding personal diaries you might not have thought of. Do whatever you feel you need to do to give yourself the freedom to open up about yourself and your feelings: there are no right or wrong answers.

Lastly, and perhaps most importantly, always remember you're not alone; even if there's no one else you can turn to, know that there are a lot of mental health communities out there. Also, keep in mind if it's to do with depression I've probably "been there, done that" at some point and will have your back if you need help.

SELF-CARE TIPS

First things first: self-care ISN'T selfish.

Self-care also isn't something you should only do when you get "everything else" done, nor is it something you should only do when you feel you "deserve" it. In fact, self-care is something that's fundamental to your personal well-being, especially when suffering from an illness. Would you think a person with cancer was selfish for practising self-care? No. And neither are you.

These are just a handful of ideas that you can adapt or build upon to suit your own needs.

+ Make your bed EVERY day (you'll always start the day with an accomplishment).
+ Get ready for the day, even if you don't plan to leave the house.
+ Be social, even if you only show up and sit in a corner to people-watch.
+ Don't listen to sad music, even if you want to. Stick to upbeat tunes.
+ Watch Netflix, but don't fall down the rabbit hole of binges.
+ Try to find some healthy food to eat.
+ Reserve comfort food to being rewards rather than being every meal.
+ Make a list of things you can do when you're overwhelmed and draw from the list during those times.
+ Choose some hobbies where you'll improve, not just gain pleasure.
+ Go outside. Seriously: it can help.
+ Pre-plan your week so you don't have to rely on making decisions based on your moods
+ Exercise, but choose something you ENJOY doing.
+ Disappear into a good book for awhile (and put down any book you're not enjoying).
+ Volunteer some time to a cause you really care about.
+ Stick up some affirmations where you'll actually see them daily.
+ Pamper yourself: self-care isn't selfish or self-indulgent.
+ Don't try to rely just on yourself to get better. There's no shame in needing help.
+ If you take medication set up a schedule with alarms or reminders so you take it regularly and on-time.
+ Spend time with animals (volunteering at shelters is great for furry friendships).
+ Play with children (or adults who remember how to play and be silly).
+ Create a Happy Box, filled with things you enjoy to stimulate your mind & senses.
+ Wear clothes which are comfortable, but also make you feel good about yourself.
+ Avoid retail therapy as a means to boost your mood.
+ Keep a chart: add a star for each day/hour you've engaged in a self-care activity.
+ Sing along loudly to an upbeat song you know the words to.
+ Dance to upbeat music, even if you feel silly to begin with.
+ Keep a separate gratitude journal and add to it daily, even if it's only one thing.
+ Make time to journal daily, even if it's for as little as five minutes.
+ Invest time & money, as you're able, towards self improvement: you're worth it!
+ Keep a mood-tracker so you can look for patterns to your moods and anticipate problems.

+ Pay It Forward: a little effort/kindness can change someone else's day and your own!
+ When changing habits, start small and build from each little success.
+ Keep your GP advised of any changes to your health: they can't help if they don't know!
+ Keep your room/space clean and tidy, it's makes a huge difference to your mood.
+ Learn to stop and smell the roses.
+ Consider depression-specific hypnotherapy, cognitive behavioural therapy (CBT) or nuero-linguistic programming (NLP) as alternatives if you're unwilling to take any prescribed medications.
+ Join a social group for people with depression, either online or offline.
+ If you can't avoid it at least try to cut back on caffeine and refined sugars.
+ Avoid self-medicating with drugs or alcohol: both will make things a lot worse in the long-run.
+ Call a help-line, talk to a therapist or someone you trust when you're overwhelmed.

ADD YOUR OWN IDEAS BELOW!

SELF-HARM ALTERNATIVES

Not everyone who's depressed self-harms, but...

It's a real and present danger to many vulnerable people worldwide. Often people immediately think of razor blades and scars when self-harm is brought up, however, it can take other forms, such as: burning, picking or reopening wounds, punching or hitting yourself, inserting objects into the skin, purposely bruising or breaking your bones, and certain types of hair pulling.

If you do self-harm, are considering starting to self-harm, or are feeling as though you might relapse into self-harming, please seek professional help IMMEDIATELY. To help get you through any impulse, consider these alternatives...

+ Draw on yourself with washable red marker, then take a shower and wash away your pain along with the ink.
+ Scribble on sheets of paper then try to find patterns and objects in the scribbles.
+ Cover yourself with band-aids in the places where you want to cut.
+ Let yourself cry, even if it's hard to start. Once you do don't stop until you're exhausted.
+ Go out and perform one act of kindness for a stranger.
+ Use Henna in place of a razor blade.
+ Rip a pile of paper into REALLY small pieces.
+ Give someone a long hug.
+ Build a pillow fort.
+ Fold paper and invent a new origami shape.
+ Draw on the walls... or paint with watercolors if you don't want permanence.
+ Go to a public place and people watch.
+ Take a really hot (but NOT scalding) bath and "be" in the moment.
+ Colour or scribble over people in magazines.
+ Buy yourself some toys and play like you're 5 years old again!
+ Squeeze ice REALLY hard.
+ Sing along loudly to an upbeat song you know the words to.
+ Play loud music and dance energetically... be as wild and uncoordinated as you like.
+ Stain the place you want to cut with fake blood or food-colouring.
+ Write words on yourself in red marker pen.
+ Scribble a word again and again to say how you're feeling e.g. 'lonely', 'angry'.
+ Watch a foreign language channel and make up your own interpretations.
+ Make a paper chain of the days it's been since you last cut (add a new one every day).
+ Figure out how to put 8 queens on a chessboard without any of them being able to kill each other (note: there are 92 possible ways to do this).
+ Keep a chart - add a star for each day/hour you haven't self-harmed.
+ Bite into a hot pepper or chew a piece of ginger root.
+ Have a pillow fight with the wall.

+ Fill a piece of paper with cross hatch drawings.
+ Write your feelings down on paper then rip it up.
+ Throw ice cubes at the bathtub wall, at a tree, etc.
+ Make a soft cloth doll to represent the things you're angry at; cut and tear it instead of yourself.
+ Put PVA/Elmer's glue on your hands then peel it off.
+ Get a hug for at least 20 seconds (long hugs help reduce stress hormones).
+ Put tiger balm on the places you want to cut (but not if the skin is broken!).
+ Count back from 500 or 1000. Start over every time you make a mistake.
+ Learn to swear in another language.
+ Make a phone list of people you can call for support. Allow yourself to use it.
+ Choose a random object, like a paper clip, and try to list 30 different uses for it.
+ Repeat to yourself "I don't deserve to be hurt" even if you don't believe it yet.
+ Try a self harm project like The Butterfly Project.
+ Call a help-line, talk to a therapist or someone you trust.

ADD YOUR OWN IDEAS BELOW!

STORY OF MY LIFE

Many people forget how complex and interesting the sequence of events that have made up their life can be from an outside perspective. The negative backlash and scorn of society against the idea of being 'unique individuals' means we end up viewing our personal story as unworthy of attention or reflection. However, when you think about it, of the 108 billion people who have lived none have experienced life in exactly the same way as you have. No one has experienced (or ever will) an identical collection of thoughts, emotions and moments of time as you. These are uniquely yours. So use the following timeline pages to construct the narrative of your life. Take your time to fill out the space with the most significant, memorable, emotional and even embarrassing moments of your life from birth to present day.

BORN

TODAY

WHAT I NEED TO HEAR MOST

Write down the words you need to hear more than anything else right now.

COLOUR ME

COLOUR ME

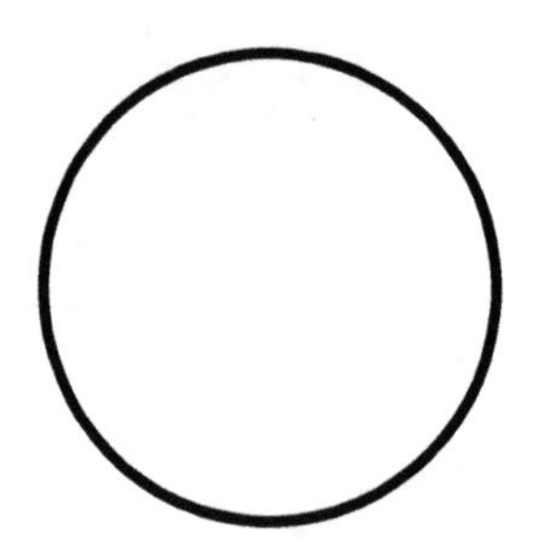

MY LIFE WEB

It's easy to feel completely alone when you're being dragged down by depression. Sometimes you give in to self-isolation because you lack motivation and your bed seems to have inexplicably manifested its own natural gravitational force. Other times you'll have a bad run of negative self-talk sniping that you're entirely unworthy of other people's time and attention, so you stop seeking out your friends and family "just in case." But one of the things depression is best at is clouding your perceptions. The truth is you aren't completely alone: your friends and family do care about you and the people you interact with every day would notice if you dropped off the face of the earth.

Physically drawing and labelling these connections can help you feel much less alone. Using the available space, map out all the relationships in your life that you can think of. Start by writing your name in the circle, then mind-map out how you're connected to everyone else in your life. These connections can be as close (your mother) or tenuous (your sister's best friend's older brother's college roommate that you met at a BBQ last summer) as you like.

ICA

N T

OPEN EYES

Draw, write or collage over + around the eye with things you WANT to show the world.

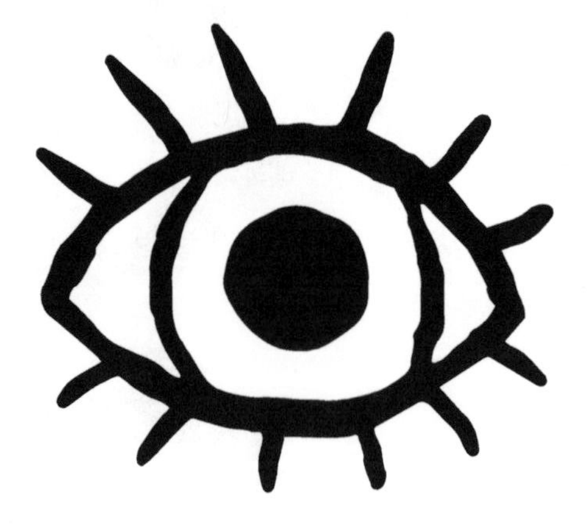

OPEN EYES - EXPLORED

Using your picture as a mental focus take a moment to consider why it's crucial that you show these things to the world. Are they your strongest values or beliefs? Are they things you feel good about? Are you proud of these things or are they the things you think the world wants or demands to see from you? Are they things you feel you have to show to fit in with your friends, peers and/or society? How do you think this affects your happiness and mental health?

CLOSED EYES

Draw, write or collage over + around the eye with things you DON'T want to show the world.

CLOSED EYES - EXPLORED

Using your picture as a mental focus take some time to consider why you consider it important to hide these things from the world. Are they values, beliefs or ideas you enjoy that you are ashamed of? Or perhaps you don't think those around you would understand? Or are they things you think the world wants or demands that you hide? Maybe they're things you feel you have to hide to fit in with your friends, peers and/or society? How do you think this affects your happiness and mental health?

WHAT I NEED TO HEAR MOST

What do I TRULY need to be content?

IT IS DURING
OUR DARKEST
MOMENTS THAT
WE MUST FOCUS
TO SEE THE LIGHT

Aristotle

BUCKET LIST

Write a list of everything you'd like to say YES to.

FUCKIT LIST

Write a list of everything you'd like to say NO to.

INSPIRE ME

Anyone else getting tired of seeing motivational quotes* everywhere? Especially when you're feeling anything but motivated? Maybe they remind you that, nine times out of ten, getting motivated even on a good day still means you're pushing yourself to do things you probably don't care about, but feel like you should because it's what you're "supposed" to be doing.

That's why this page is about INSPIRATION. Think about who or what inspires you... it can come from anywhere you like: books to websites, quotes to people, art to fashion and everything in-between. Just remember: they don't have to be things that result in anything outwardly productive or transformational in your life, they only have to bring you a sense of contentment.

Then fill these pages with writing, drawings, photos or a collage of all three to represent all the things you feel inspired by that you can refer back to when you hit a particularly rough patch.

*we'll just ignore that the journal has some motivational quotes in it, okay?

WORRY VAULT

Bad things are bound to happen and suck as it might that's just the way things will sometimes go. Brooding about them only makes it worse because you'll just end up chasing the Worry Rabbit down the Hole of Catastrophizing, where the worst possible outcome of any situation becomes the only conceivable outcome available. This is the time when we tend to do or say the things we'll regret later.

Use these pages when you need to get a worry out of your head: Start by writing, without stopping, everything that's churning around in your head at the moment. Once it's all out on the page give yourself permission to leave it in your journal. If you feel it's vital to come back to it, do so in no less than a week, so you don't feel so emotionally raw and have hopefully gained some perspective on the issue(s).

BODY LOVE

Modern society's obsession with beauty standards, coupled with its deep-running stigma against disabilities (visible & invisible), makes it far too easy to get stuck in an internal loop of a toxic body (& mind) hate. It's time to write your body a long overdue Thank You letter for everything it does for you and admiring the differences which make your body unique to you.

DEAR BODY ____________________

LOVE, ____________________

COLOUR ME

YOU SAY YOU'RE

BROKEN

BUT CRACKS ARE HOW

THE LIGHT GETS IN

MENTAL MONSTER

Just as no two people will ever experience depression precisely the same way, every person's depression monster is unique to them. Perhaps this is the first time you've met the nasty little critter. Maybe it's been such a long time companion you can predict it better than you can predict yourself. Either way, use this space to create a picture that's representative of your depression and add its name beneath.

ONCE UPON A TIME

Write a short narrative about hunting your depression as if it were a real monster.

Take your time to research your monster: study its preferred feeding grounds (e.g. triggers), and describe its behaviours (symptoms) before revealing some of its weaknesses (e.g. therapy, medication, self-care, etc.).

Next, write out your ambush in the story and stage a bloody coup. Use as much or as little detail as you want and come back to add more to your narrative as things change, reshaping and remoulding your monster and weapons as needed.

MOTTO ME

Pick a positive motto or saying you'd like to live your life by.

Reflect on the reasons why you chose this particular motto. Questions you might like to consider include: why is it essential for you to live your life by these words? Which of your core values are represented by this motto? Do you live by this motto and its ideals now? Or are there changes you need to make to follow them more closely?

Take your chosen motto and create a piece of art either around it or that represents it.

THE CLUTTERED HOARD

If you've ever spent any time lurking in the murky depths of The Total Blah, you'll know how easy it is to let a lot of things pile up (not just that growing mound of ripe-smelling clothes which is now a home-grown experiment in evolution). This can include the mental and emotional clutter we collect and hold onto the tightest when trapped in the dark.

Unfortunately, Stuff doesn't always make us happier. In fact, having too much around can make things even worse. Take some time to explore: how much stuff is too much? Have you ever experienced this problem? Is clutter just limited to material goods, or does it exist in other forms, perhaps in the digital world? Do you think your life might be better off without this Stuff? How could you reduce this kind of clutter?

UNCONDITIONAL

Use this page to create a piece of artwork that represents what unconditional love looks or feels like to you.

UNCONDITIONAL - EXPLORED

We all have a basic human need to connect with other peopleand to feel we belong. For some connection comes from family and intimate relationships. Those who don't have a supportive family or a significant other will build their own unique families. People need love: our lives just seem to work better when we love and are loved. So, explore your thoughts on unconditional love and what it means to you.

MEDICINE MINE

Taking (or not) medication can be a sensitive topic for anyone battling with depression. There will never be one right way, and the decision will always be deeply personal and probably take a long time to work through and accept, both consciously and subconsciously. If you do take medication for your depression draw your relationship with it. If you haven't started any medication or have chosen not to use any, then use the space to draw your thoughts and feelings about it.

TO LOVE

ONESELF

IS THE BEGINNING OF A

LIFELONG ROMANCE

Oscar Wilde

COLOUR ME

ACT OF COMPASSION

It takes effort, patience, and compassion to love someone with depression... especially when that person is yourself. It's time to take a step back and describe a way you've shown compassion and supported a friend recently. When you've finished, you can use this as a basis of how you can do the same for yourself.

A DAY WITHOUT

Write about a time in your life when you didn't feel depressed. When was it? What was happening? Write about it in as much detail as you can, for example: how did your mind feel? How sensations can you remember experiencing with your body? What activities were you involved in? Who were you with? Engage all your senses when writing about it.

CRAPPY DAY PEP TALK

This exercise is excellent preparation for those days when you're faced with the feeling of being sucked into the squalid depths of emotional doom.

The next time you're feeling stable or a little like your old self, write yourself a pep talk full of praise, affirmations and encouraging self-talk. Then you can come back and read it on a bad day to give yourself a little emotional boost.

If you haven't seen even a minor stable day in a long stretch, turn to a close friend who you can trust and ask them to write the pep talk for you. Ask them to include some of the things they think are unique, praise-worthy and just plain awesome about you. Remember to stick the pep talk in your journal so you can read through it when things are feeling particularly grim.

MY INNER CRITIC

It's probably surprising to learn that your inner critic (that annoying little voice that has only negative things to say and just gets louder and more insistent when we're depressed) thinks it's helping you. Your inner critic is part of your "ego defence mechanism" set, which exists to protect us from things like surprise, hurts or disappointments. It's based on a mix of learned behaviours and beliefs picked up from outside sources (i.e. parents, teachers, peers, etc.). Unfortunately, self-esteem and self-image are developed by how we talk to ourselves and how we THINK of ourselves. For a lot of people, their inner critic isn't rational, constructive or healthy. Depression just adds fuel to this fire.

To help silence your inner critic you need to both personalise and externalise it as a "living" entity that's a separate being from yourself. But, unlike your depression, remember your inner critic ISN'T a monster: it merely thinks it's doing you a favour. Consider it more like an unhelpful guest, irritating sibling or out-of-touch politician. Use this space to create a visual image of your own bratty, nagging inner critic and give it a correspondingly obnoxious name.

CRITIC'S REVIEW

Our society is often based upon impossible perfectionism, so it can help to give yourself permission to be human and know you're doing your best in your current situation. In order to do this you need to take the time to have a heart-to-heart talk with your inner critic. If it's been telling you all the things you've been doing wrong lately, then reply with all the things you've been doing right. If it's been overly opinionated write down your best comebacks and throw some shade its way before sending it to a corner for a time out.

DOODLE DAYS

Contrary to the old school of thought, researchers have found doodling isn't a waste of time and is good for our brains. Many people find doodling an enjoyable activity that relieves stress,.It also distract us from consciously worrying about our problems while opening us up to subconsciously processing these issues. It can you help improve focus and concentration, which is a definite win since those two things typically take a hike when your depression gets uppity. So, pick up your pen when you start to feel stressed and start doodling until you've filled this entire space up!

COLOUR ME

COLOUR ME

FORGIVENESS LIST

We all struggle with the unpleasant feelings of shame, anger or unworthiness from time to time, but they can be magnified during a bout of depression. A Forgiveness List is a simple method to help you lessen some of those feelings. Write a list of everything you believe you need forgiveness for. The list is only for your eyes, so don't be afraid to put anything on it, big or small. When it's complete, take a black marker pen and scribble over each entry until they're completely covered. As each one is covered forgive yourself and let go of the corresponding anger, shame or sense of unworthiness.

(write it down)

100 THINGS THAT

MAKE ME HAPPY

CHARACTER CUE

Great role models are important, and there's no rule to say they have to be real people. Imagine your favourite fictional character is dealing with the same problems you're facing at the moment. Then try to figure out how they would solve them.*

By having characters you strongly admire or connect with take on your fears, problems or disabilities you can sometimes reveal a creative solution to a tricky issue you're facing.

*Try to choose a positive role model & avoid characters whose main problem solving technique is violence.

REACHING BACK

What if your hands could tell stories?
Trace your hand onto this page and fill it with images that represent your past.

REACHING FORWARD

What if your hands could tell stories?
Trace your hand onto this page and fill it with images of your hopes for the future.

I DON'T WANT TO WRITE ABOUT...

This will probably feel weird at first, but try to write about what you DON'T want to write about in this (or any other) journal. Don't think, don't edit... just list everything that comes to mind. Free write until you run out of steam, then go back over what you've listed and explore why you don't want to commit these things to paper.

To help understand what you're still holding in, the underlying motivations and potential solutions ask yourself some of the following questions. Is it because you don't want to think about these particular things? Are these things still too painful or raw to deal with right now? Are you afraid that putting it on paper will make it more (or less) real for you? Are you having issues with privacy which you might need to find solutions to?

SING TO ME

Pick some lyrics from your favourite UPLIFTING songs and illustrate them.

SURVIVAL STRATEGIES

Sometimes depression demands you just survive it, riding out the black waves of doom until things are a little more stable... or at least no so hellish. No matter whether things are black or grey, everyone has their favourite survival strategies to just get through the day.

What secret strategies do you use for getting through life in spite of your depression? When do you use these strategies: at school, work, home, with friends or elsewhere? Are they effective? Are they safe? Would you recommend them to others? Why or why not? Can you imagine using these strategies forever, or are they just helpful at this point in your life? Are you open to finding new ones?

DEPRESSION
IS A FLAW IN
BRAIN CHEMISTRY
NOT
CHARACTER

COLOUR ME

COMPLIMENT COLLECTION

Use these pages to write down any compliments you've received, big or small. Continue to add to your collection whenever you receive a new compliment and use these pages for a positive boost when you're having one of those shitty days where nothing seems to be going right.

GRATITUDE

Engaging in gratitude when you're depressed can be hard. On your angry-at-the-world days, your brain doesn't like to admit you have anything to be grateful for and on your beat-yourself-up days, it tries to drown you in guilt because there are lots of things to be thankful for so you 'shouldn't' be depressed in the first place. Both these situations are just your monster using your inner critic as a sock puppet.

Try not to think of gratitude as a guilt-trip or shaming. Instead, reframe it as a means to reduce a multitude of toxic emotions your monster is feeding on. As a bonus practising gratitude is also strongly correlated with increased happiness, optimism, and self-esteem, all of which can be in pretty short supply when you're down. Use these pages to visually document all the things in your life you're grateful for.

(INTER)CONNECTIVITY

The world is connected as never before and, more often than not, we don't give it a second thought. What is YOUR relationship with media: do you like how you use phones, computers, and digital entertainment?

Write about any or all of the following: if you're online a lot what activities do you find take up the most of your time? Which do you enjoy? Which ones nurture you, expose you to positive role models or make you feel emotionally stronger? Which ones do you think are necessary and which ones are merely time-wasters? Do any expose you to negative influences or make you feel worse than when you logged on (google "Facebook depression")? Are there any hashtags you've stumbled across on social media that have had some emotional impact on you? Were these positive or negative experiences?

POSITIVE EXPERIENCES

When our head gets preoccupied with all the *bad* experiences we've had it's easy to forget the positive experiences and behaviours that we've engaged in. Take some time to look *back* through your life for those times when you've displayed the following qualities in acts that can be big OR small. You can then use these pages to remind yourself of these positives the next time your inner critic is trying to convince you everything you do is wrong or *bad*.

Courage: ______________________________

____

____

Kindness: ______________________________

____

____

Unconditional Love: ______________________________

____

____

Selflessness: ______________________________

____

____

Sacrifice: ______________________________

____

____

Forgiveness: ______________________________

____

____

Wisdom: ______________________________

____

____

Honesty: __________

Integrity: __________

Self Respect: __________

Cooperation: __________

Community Spirit: __________

Trustworthiness: __________

Independence: __________

Tolerance: __________

Passion: __________

LIKE
TO
LEARN

(write it down)

100 THINGS I'D

COLOUR ME

MY SAFE SPACE

Everyone has a different definition of what "safe" is. What do you picture in your head when you think of the word "safe" and yourself at the same time? Use this space visually create this mental safe place.

FOREVER MOMENTS

We all have moments in our life that have such a significant impact on shaping who we are that we'll never forget them. What are some amazing, POSITIVE moments in your life that will stay with you forever? Describe them and what makes them so completely unforgettable in as much detail as you can.

Whenever you're having a particularly bad or stressful day turn to these pages and re-read a memory of your choice. After you've finished, use what you've read as your starting point to mentally visualize that memory. Allow the positive emotions associated with it to eventually outweigh your bad day funk.

THOSE NEGATIVE THOUGHTS

These two pages are simply for you to write down (or draw out) any negative thoughts you might have. These pages serve a dual purpose:

1. To get the thoughts out of your head, but not for dwelling on them.
2. To allow yourself to acknowledge the existence of these negative thoughts and then let them go once they've been physically written down.

WHAT'S REALLY EATING YOU?

Anyone who has experienced depression can relate to how your conscience blows things out of proportion, causing you to feel disproportionately guilty and remorseful. So it might be time to take stock and see whether you're merely "should-ing" all over yourself and ending up in a worse state of mind. Ask yourself: are there any events in your life you feel guilty about missing because of your depression?

Then explore: are you feeling guilty because you want(ed) to be there? Is it possible your guilt might be caused by outside pressures and expectations of what you "should" want to do? Do I feel you have to do these things to make others happy? Do these things even make you happy when you're NOT depressed?

COAT OF ARMS

Everyone is the hero of their story, and every hero needs a coat of arms. Choose symbols you feel represent your unique traits and strengths and incorporate them into your unique coat of arms. Add a motto along the outside edge that can either be your motto from your MOTTO ME page or another one you feel represents your values and ideals.

HERALDIC DESIGNS

Reflection: consider why you chose the elements of your heraldic design, including the motto. What does each of these components mean to you? What do they represent? How does your motto tie into your design? How does your heraldic design make you feel? Use your coat of arms to help remind yourself to be the HERO of your own story.

THERE'S NO REASON TO BE ASHAMED OF YOUR STORY

FINISH DOODLING HERE

START DOODLING HERE

ESCAPING THE MONSTER

Visualization can be a powerful tool, especially when we alter an image and change the outcome (and our thoughts) in the process. Imagine your depression as a scenario where you're locked in a room with your monster: draw what you see. Then, imagine you're given the means to escape this place and alter the picture you initially drew to reflect this change.

DEAR FUTURE ME...

Write a letter to your future self. Pick an age for your future self: this will help you define the goals and overall content of your message. Assume that your future self will be your ideal future, but understand that, realistically, life will probably have a few hiccups along the way. Adopt a casual tone and remember to use "I" language when talking about your current self and use "you" language when talking about your future self.

Take a little time to summarise your current self, just a quick reminder of who you currently are. Include your dreams, hopes, and goals. Don't forget to note down what you feel are your fears (what you can control) and limitations (what is outside your control) at this time.

Then ask your future self some questions about your future life, but remember to keep them specific. Don't ask "Are you still depressed?" but try something like "How amazing is it not to feel depressed all the time?" instead.

DEAR FUTURE ME

FROM: PRESENT DAY ME

FROM FUTURE ME...

Write a letter to your present-day self from your future self. Date it five years from now and then write it as if those five years have gone exactly as you want them to. Be as specific as possible with the details as you can. Keep it positive and only list those things you WANT to have happened. While this might seem a little odd, this type of exercise can allow you to visualise a more positive future on a subconscious level, which in turn can subtly influence your current moods and behaviours.

TO PRESENT DAY ME

FROM: FUTURE ME

RORSCHACH

Create your Rorschach by adding a little ink or paint to the centre of this page and then folding it in half. Unfold the page and leave your journal open in a safe (private) place so the ink/paint can dry. Then use the white space around the ink blot you've created to describe what you see and how it makes you feel.

CHANGING FOCUS

We've been led to believe that setting goals is essential to a wellness routine or giving yourself a sense of purpose when you might otherwise be floundering. However, making goals when you're in the midst of a depressive episode is very different to when your mood is stable, especially because your ILLNESS changes your range of function. This type of h goal setting will often end up with you comparing yourself to others or to how you were pre-depression. Plus, and any goal, no matter how small, that you fail to accomplish will make you MORE depressed. So, FORGET setting goals for the moment.

Instead, take time to write down areas of your life that you'd like to FOCUS on. For example, instead of making it a goal to ditch the junk and only eat healthy food CHANGE YOUR FOCUS to making tiny, but healthy changes to your diet over time. Maybe have a little more fruit or veggies. Consider dropping one caffeinated or sugary drink a day. Start small, drill deep. Find the little things you feel you can shift in a positive way. The best part is tiny changes have a snowball effect hat an lead to BIG changes to your lifestyle and your depression.

So, write down what you'd like to focus on and the tiny changes you might like to try. Then, when you realize you've unconsciously developed a new, healthy habit by focusing on making that tiny change, write it down and celebrate. However, don't sweat it if you lose focus for a while..simply try again tomorrow if you're up to it.

Recovering isn't a race or a competition.

COLOUR ME

COMIC STRIPS

There's nothing humorous about having depression, but humour itself can be very beneficial towards alleviating the symptoms. Enjoy some levity through focusing in on your own life and drawing some comic strips about some of the funniest moments you've experienced or witnessed.

SO, THIS ONE TIME...

Helping others can make us happy while giving us a sense of purpose and satisfaction at the same time... all things that get a little suffocated during any down period. Write down the story of a time you made a positive difference in someone's life by helping them in some way. How did you change them for the better? How did it change you? Consider what you think this reflects about you as a person.

THE VICTORIES

Use these pages to list your accomplishments and victories, big and small, as they happen. This way you can look back at what you've already accomplished and can give yourself the confidence that you can do these things again. Just keep in mind that on those days when only being human is almost asking too much then, yes, getting out of bed can be counted as a victory!

MY GREATEST COMFORT

Hopefully it isn't too surprising that comfort is very useful in coping with depression; it provides a form of relief from the emotional and physical symptoms of the illness. Comfort comes in all shapes and sizes, whether it's a physical item, activity, person or belief system. What is YOUR greatest comfort? Take the time to describe it in as much detail as possible and explain why it helps you when things get rough.

MIRROR MIRROR (PRESENT)

Collage or draw over the mirror a representation of what you see when you look at your reflection now.

MIRROR MIRROR (FUTURE)

Collage or draw over the mirror a representation of what you want to see when you look at your reflection in the future.

INNER ANTHEMS - THE PLAYLIST

Music is a powerful thing: it can help us feel alive and connected to the world around us, it can help us to identify and express emotions, and it promotes wellness and manages stress. However, while it can be beneficial to listen to music, to help express how you're feeling or which allows you to vent difficult thoughts and emotions you're experiencing, sometimes it can make you feel worse. So, tread with caution...

Keep a log/playlist of the songs that speak to you to make it easier to remember which ones triggered a particular emotional response in you.

INNER ANTHEMS - EXPLORED

You can actively and intentionally select and use the music you listen to become more in control of your feelings and gain emotional stability. Use your song log as a guide to find out how music affects you and explore the following questions: does the music allow you to sit with, change or set a new mood? Does the music make you feel better or worse? When is it not helpful? Is there a specific style of music that is helpful or unhelpful? Or perhaps there are individual artists or words used in a song which have different effects on your mood?

What's the point? By considering these questions, you can help yourself work out which music you should listen to (and when) to reap the most significant emotional benefits.

START DOODLING HERE

FINISH DOODLING HERE

PROVE
THEM
WRONG

TAKEN FOR GRANTED

It's ridiculously easy to take things for granted... until they aren't there anymore. Challenge yourself to think about all things in your everyday life that you've taken for granted, even something as mundane and overlooked as breathing. Learn to appreciate these things again by devoting this space to them using a combination of words and art.

APPLES & ORANGES - EXPOSED

What do apples and oranges have to do with anything? A lot of misery is caused by thinking we don't "measure up" and ignoring the chance to become all that we can if only we were focusing on our uniqueness. Keeping apples and oranges in mind can help you to avoid comparing yourself with others in your dating relationships, friendships, family, and at school or work.

Now, it's time to prove the futility of comparisons...

NAME TWO WELL-KNOWN SINGERS, BOTH POPULAR, BUT VERY DIFFERENT:

NAME TWO POPULAR ACTORS, BOTH TALENTED, BUT IN DIFFERENT WAYS:

NAME TWO GREAT ATHLETES, BOTH PROFESSIONAL, BUT IN DIFFERENT SPORTS:

NAME TWO POPULAR AUTHORS, BOTH BESTSELLERS, BUT IN DIFFERENT GENRES:

NAME TWO ARTISTS, BOTH FAMOUS, BUT IN DIFFERENT STYLES OF ART:

NAME TWO BANDS, BOTH SUCCESSFUL, BUT IN DIFFERENT TYPES OF MUSIC:

NAME TWO BOOKS, BOTH BEST-SELLERS, BUT FROM DIFFERENT GENRES:

APPLES & ORANGES - EXPLORED

Can you think of any times when you've fallen into the comparison trap? Take some time to consider WHY you compared yourself the way you did and then explore the ways you might be able to reframe your thoughts whenever you catch yourself doing it again by keeping the idea of 'apples and oranges' in mind.

MINDFULNESS

Lots of people like to suggest meditation, but when you're depressed the last place you want to go hang out is in your head where your monster is lurking. Mindfulness is an alternative you can fit into your everyday schedule. By deliberately and carefully choosing to devote your mind and your senses to an 'immediate experience' and noting everything that's happening right then and there you can start shutting your mind down for a time while providing yourself with a sense of calmness and centring.

Use the following pages to write about the act of writing and focus on the sensation of the writing itself. Think and write about the body movements needed to write, the way you're sitting, the sound of your pen moving across the paper, the smell of the journal, the sight of your thoughts appearing as writing on the page, the feeling of the pen pinched between your fingers, the way you're breathing changes the longer you write, the small nuances of your surrounding environment, etc.

Bonus: this exercise can be repeated whenever you feel the need to calm your mind and bring yourself into the now, with the topic being tweaked to keep your interest.

SYMPTOM COLLAGE

Sometimes there can be aspects of our depression and the range of symptoms it causes (physically, mentally and emotionally) that are just too damn hard to verbalise. In these situations, it can help to use IMAGES to portray our triggers or symptoms visually. Use the following pages to draw or collage an image that represents the parts of your depression that you find the hardest to deal with and talk about.

A LETTER YOU'LL NEVER SEND

Still angry or upset with someone in your life? Writing a letter might help.

There's a therapeutic release that comes from writing something down. By organising your thoughts in a coherent form, you can validate, acknowledge, and lessen some of your own negative emotions that might be hindering your ability to let go and heal. Remember: the purpose of the letter ISN'T to send it, it's the benefits of the act of creating it that you're after.

TO: ______________________________

FROM: ______________________

MOTIVATE ME

Okay, yes, being flooded by motivational quotes when you're depressed can be even more irritating than a bad wifi connection. But picking ones that resonate with you personally can make them meaningful and powerful (and less annoying!) in such a way as to change the way you're thinking, helping you strive towards the things you want to overcome.

So, bite the bullet and choose your favourite motivational quotes (or some rude ones if it'll make you smile on a bad day!) and then decorate them with doodles and bright colours that will give you a pick me up the next time you're having a crappy day.

COLOUR ME

COLOUR ME

CLIMBING MOUNTAINS

Your past achievements can help give you the confidence to pursue your future goals. List THREE things you've done that you never thought you'd be able to do.

Ask yourself: how did starting these things make me feel? How did I work through those feelings? How did it feel when I managed to do these things, despite the nagging of my depression or inner critic? Then explore how you could apply these insights to other things you'd like to accomplish...

MINDFULNESS ART

Pick a pencil or pen to use, hold it against the journal page and close your eyes. Spend some time checking in with yourself and going through how your depression feels in your body. Take note of where you're currently feeling a particularly strong physical sensation or symptom of your depression and how you recognise it.

Next, begin to draw a continuous squiggle without lifting your pen or pencil from the paper. While drawing imagine your depression is physically expressing itself on the page. Stop when the movement or expression feels complete. If you find yourself unable to let go of the need to control the actions of your pen/pencil try using your non-dominant hand.

When you're done open your eyes and take a close look at what you've drawn until you see an image emerge. Turn your journal side-to-side or upside down if necessary. Then, using other colours or materials, continue to develop the image until you feel it's complete. When complete tell yourself that you're allowing the emotion that guided the artwork to be released out of yourself and into the picture.

IF YOU'RE GOING THROUGH HELL

. . .

KEEP GOING

WINSTON CHURCHILL

COLOUR ME

MOOD DOODLES & TRIGGER LOGS - INSTRUCTIONS

Do a doodle each day that represents your rimary emotional state that day and track your moods over the month to see if there are any patterns. While it's best to fill in the mood doodle on the right day while your feelings are fresh, there is nothing wrong with missing a day or two and coming back to them later.

Also, by identifying your triggers, you take the first step towards gaining control and getting a better understanding of what might help you, what hurts you and what you might need to get outside help to deal with.

Triggers can come in a variety of forms, from thoughts and feelings to events and even objects. They're unique to an individual, and you're under no obligation to explain or rationalise them to anyone.

Try to keep a concise list of the various triggers you notice during the month, both good and bad. Also try to remember to note the time, place and anything else you think might be relevant.

Try not to think of the doodles and logs as homework, but a means to continue the process of transforming yourself into an active participant in your well-being.

MOOD DOODLES: JANUARY

Do a doodle each day that represents how you felt that day and track your moods over the month to see if there are any patterns.

1	2	3	4	5	6	7
8	9	10	11	12	13	14
15	16	17	18	19	20	21
22	23	24	25	26	27	28
29	30	31				

TRIGGERS: JANUARY

MOOD DOODLES: FEBRUARY

Do a doodle each day that represents how you felt that day and track your moods over the month to see if there are any patterns.

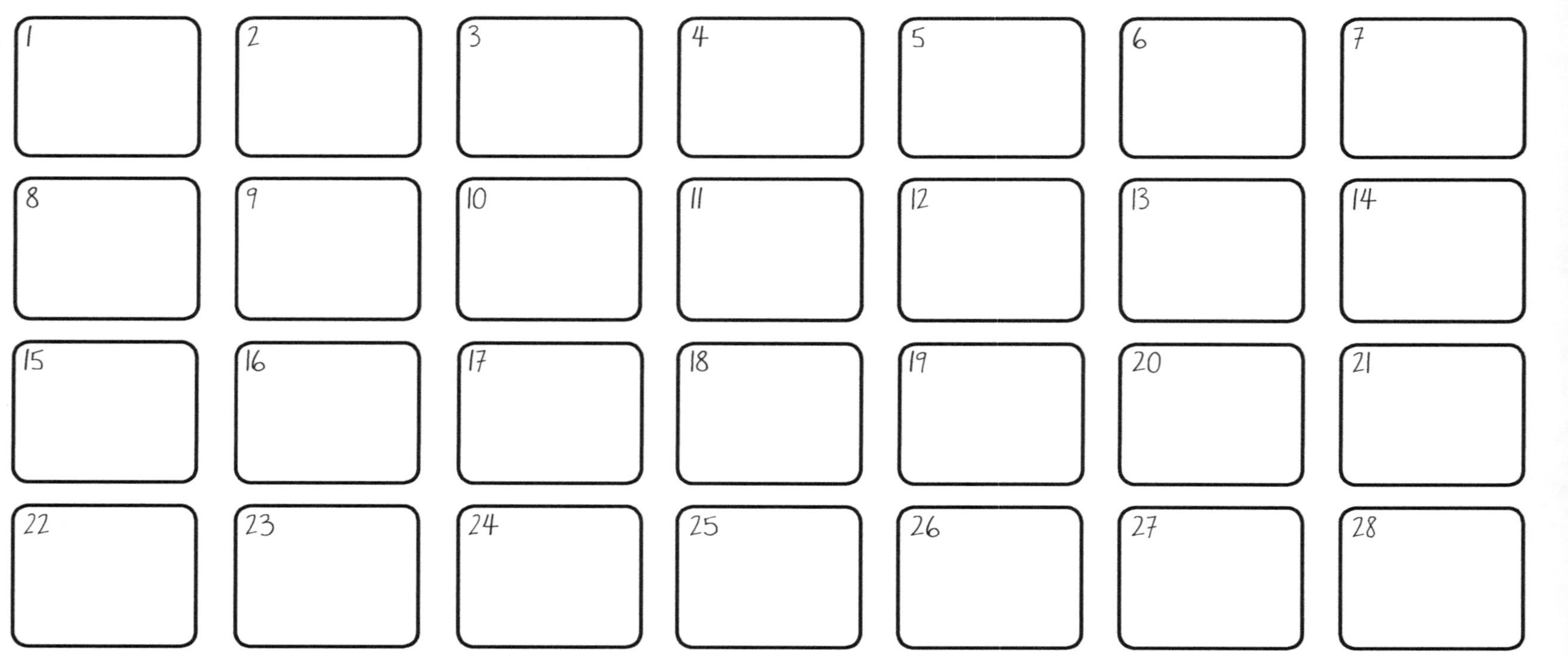

TRIGGERS: FEBRUARY

MOOD DOODLES: MARCH

Do a doodle each day that represents how you felt that day and track your moods over the month to see if there are any patterns.

1	2	3	4	5	6	7
8	9	10	11	12	13	14
15	16	17	18	19	20	21
22	23	24	25	26	27	28
29	30	31				

TRIGGERS: MARCH

MOOD DOODLES: APRIL

Do a doodle each day that represents how you felt that day and track your moods over the month to see if there are any patterns.

1	2	3	4	5	6	7
8	9	10	11	12	13	14
15	16	17	18	19	20	21
22	23	24	25	26	27	28
29	30					

TRIGGERS: APRIL

MOOD DOODLES: MAY

Do a doodle each day that represents how you felt that day and track your moods over the month to see if there are any patterns.

1	2	3	4	5	6	7
8	9	10	11	12	13	14
15	16	17	18	19	20	21
22	23	24	25	26	27	28
29	30	31				

TRIGGERS: MAY

MOOD DOODLES: JUNE

Do a doodle each day that represents how you felt that day and track your moods over the month to see if there are any patterns.

TRIGGERS: JUNE

MOOD DOODLES: JULY

Do a doodle each day that represents how you felt that day and track your moods over the month to see if there are any patterns.

1	2	3	4	5	6	7
8	9	10	11	12	13	14
15	16	17	18	19	20	21
22	23	24	25	26	27	28
29	30	31				

TRIGGERS: JULY

MOOD DOODLES: AUGUST

Do a doodle each day that represents how you felt that day and track your moods over the month to see if there are any patterns.

1	2	3	4	5	6	7
8	9	10	11	12	13	14
15	16	17	18	19	20	21
22	23	24	25	26	27	28
29	30	31				

TRIGGERS: AUGUST

MOOD DOODLES: SEPTEMBER

Do a doodle each day that represents how you felt that day and track your moods over the month to see if there are any patterns.

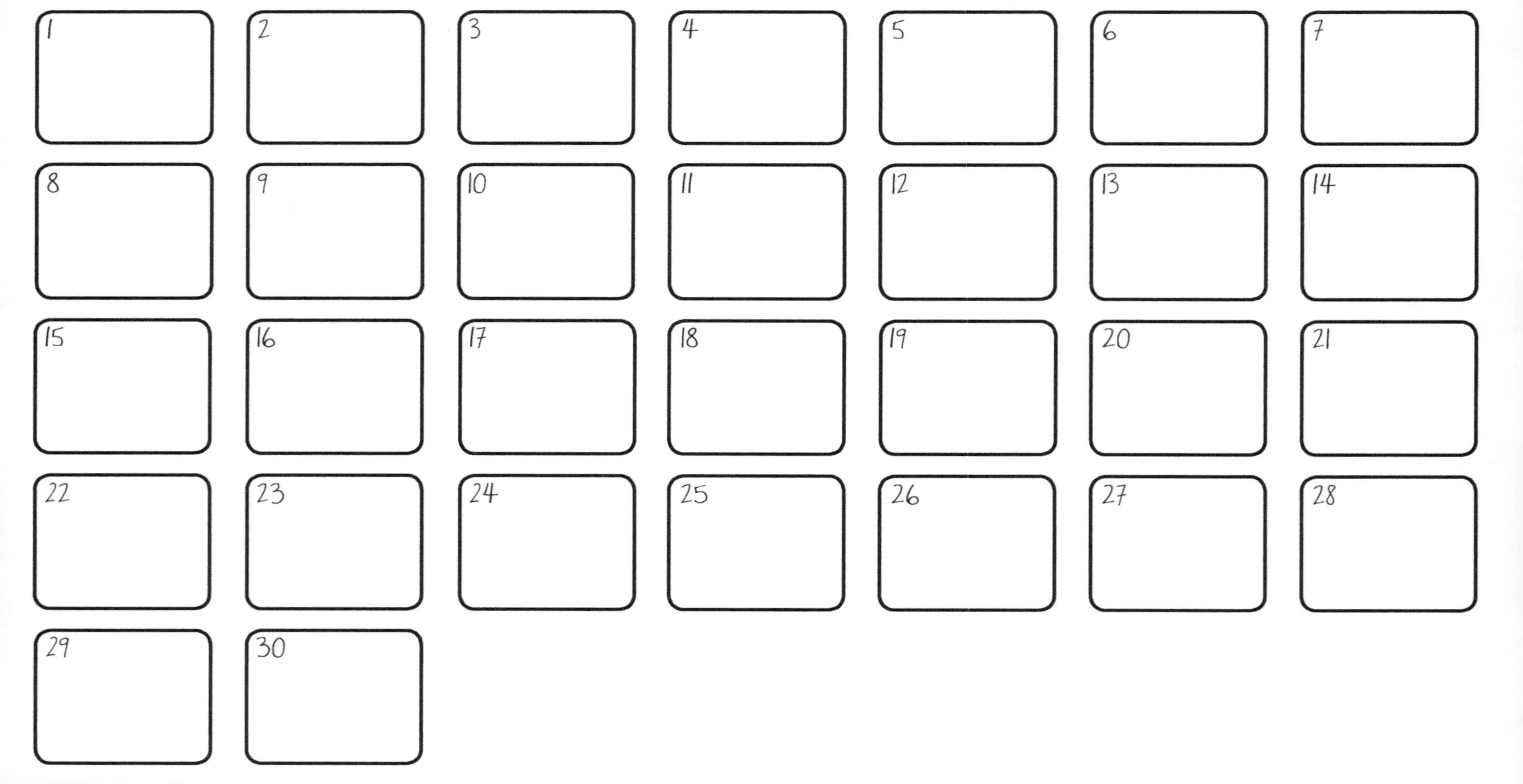

TRIGGERS: SEPTEMBER

MOOD DOODLES: OCTOBER

Do a doodle each day that represents how you felt that day and track your moods over the month to see if there are any patterns.

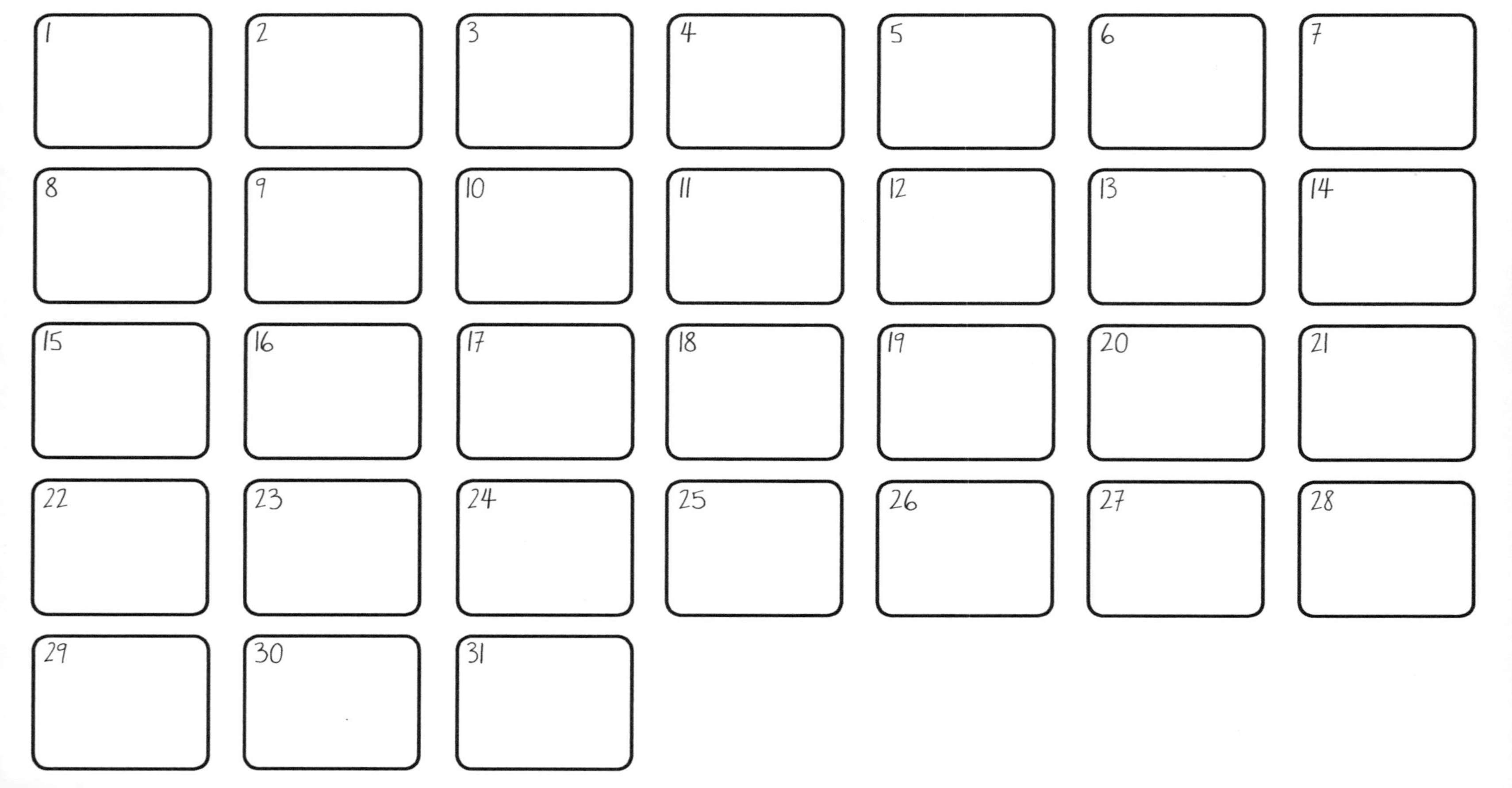

TRIGGERS: OCTOBER

MOOD DOODLES: NOVEMBER

Do a doodle each day that represents how you felt that day and track your moods over the month to see if there are any patterns.

1	2	3	4	5	6	7
8	9	10	11	12	13	14
15	16	17	18	19	20	21
22	23	24	25	26	27	28
29	30					

TRIGGERS: NOVEMBER

MOOD DOODLES: DECEMBER

Do a doodle each day that represents how you felt that day and track your moods over the month to see if there are any patterns.

1	2	3	4	5	6	7
8	9	10	11	12	13	14
15	16	17	18	19	20	21
22	23	24	25	26	27	28
29	30	31				

TRIGGERS: DECEMBER

COLOUR ME

COLOUR ME

RESOURCES

There might come a time when you need to reach out and talk to someone who isn't a friend or relative... or even your regular doctor. These groups are also excellent sources of info and resources when you need to know more, grab some quick advice, or even learn how to safely connect online to others in the same situation as you're facing.

To start with here are a few of the best-known organisations, helplines and charities which offer immediate counselling, advice and support to young adults who suffer from mental illnesses such as depression who might need someone to talk to right away.

It's OK not to be okay. It's OK to reach out for help.

AUSTRALIA

beyondblue - (beyondblue.org.au) - 1300 224 636
Black Dog Institute - (blackdoginstitute.org.au)
eHeadspace - (eheadspace.org.au) - 1800 650 890
GROW - (grow.org.au) - 1800 558 268
Headspace - (headspace.org.au)
Kids Helpline - (kidshelpline.com.au) - 1800 55 1800
Lifeline - 13 11 14
Suicide Call Back Service - (suicidecallbackservice.org.au) - 1300 659 467

CANADA

Kids Help Phone - (kidshelpphone.ca) - 1 800 668 6868
LGBT Youth Line - 1 800 268 9688
Mental Health Helpine - (mentalhealthhelpline.ca) - 1 866 531 2600
mindyourmind - (mindyourmind.ca)
Revivre - (revivre.org) - 1 866 738 4873
The Mix - (themix.org.uk)- 0808 808 4994

NEW ZEALAND

Depression Helpline - (depression.org.nz) - 0800 111 757 or TXT 4202
Kidsline - 0800 543 754
Lifeline Aotearoa - (lifeline.org.nz) - 0800 543 354
Suicide Crisis Helpline - 0508 828 865
Youthline - youthline.co.nz - 0800 376 633 or TXT 234

UNITED KINGDOM

Child Line - 0800 1111
HOPElineUK - (papyrus-uk.org) - 0800 068 4141
Mind - (mind.org.uk) - 0300 123 3393 or TXT 86463
SANE - (sane.org.uk) - 0300 304 7000
The Samaritans - 0845 790 9090

USA

Crisis Text Line - TXT "support" to 741741
National Alliance on Mental Illness (NAMI) - (nami.org) - 1800 950 6264
National Suicide Prevention Lifeline - 1 800 273 8255 or 1800 784 2433
National Suicide Prevention Lifeline TTY/TDD services - 1800 799 4889
National Youth Crisis Hotline - 1800 448 4663
Trevor Lifeline - (thetrevorproject.org) - 866 488 7386
Safe Place (nationalsafeplace.org) - for help TXT "safe" & location to 69866

ONLINE

IMAline - (imalive.org)
Random Acts Crisis Support Network - (randomacts.org)
To Write Love On Her Arms (TWLOHA) - (twloha.com)
The Blurt Foundation (blurtitout.org)
Teen Line (teenlineonline.org)
WHATWORKS4U.org (whatworks4u.org)

USEFUL HASHTAGS

#AlwaysKeepFighting
#WhatYouDontSee
#StopTheStigma
#MentalHealthAwareness
#IAmEnough
#MentalHealth
#NoKiddingMeToo
#Spoonie
#TWLOHA
#SuicidePrevention
#DepressionAwareness
#NoStigma
#IAmAWarriorBecause
#OkToSay
#DepressionRecovery
#SickNotWeak
#MadPride
#StayAlive
#SelfCare
#MentalHealthMonday
#ProjectSemicolon
#MentalHealthMatters
#MyDepressionLooksLike

BLOGS & WEBSITES

There are a LOT of blogs and websites out there for or by people who have depression, as well as groups and nonprofits that support people with a mental illness. This is by no means a complete list, but it should give you a good start if you're interested in finding valuable resources or connecting with others who understand what it means to have depression. Keep in mind that Google is your friend if you can't see anything on this pages that are specific to your location.

In no particular order:

Orygen Youth Health- (oyh.org.au)
Erika's Lighthouse - (erikaslighthouse.org)
Befrienders International - (www.befrienders.org)
Dr. Deb - (drdeborahserani.blogspot.com)
Families for Depression Awareness - (familyaware.org)
A Splintered Mind - (douglascootey.com)
Pick the Brain - (pickthebrain.com)
SANE Australia - (sane.org)
Blue Light Blue - (bluelightblue.com)
Chipur - (chipur.com)
The Jason Foundation - (jasonfoundation.com)
DepressedTeens - (depressedteens.com)
Wing of Madness - (wingofmadness.com)
The TeenScreen National Center for Mental Health Checkups - (teenscreen.org)
Depression Forums - (depressionforums.org)
Young Minds (youngminds.org.uk)
Depression & Mental Illness Resource - (depressionresource.tumblr.com)
Depression Army - (depressionarmy.com/ourblog)
Time to Change - (time-to-change.org.uk)
Very Important Kids - (vik.org.uk)
The Mighty - (themighty.com)
Creatives Aga;nst Stigma - (creativesagainstdepression.com)
I Need A Lighthouse - (ineedalighthouse.org)
Papyrus - (papyrus-uk.org)
Rethink Mental Illness - (rethink.org)
LIVIN - (livin.org.au)
Turn2Me - (turn2me.org)
Attitudes in Reverse - (attitudesinreverse.org)
The Reach Foundation - (reach.org.au)
Born This Way - (bornthisway.foundation)
Students Against Depression - (studentsagainstdepression.org)
The Low Down - (thelowdown.co.nz)
SPEAK: Suicide Prevention Education Awareness for Kids - (speakforthem.org)
Adolescent Self Injury Foundation - (adolescentselfinjuryfoundation.org)

COLOUR ME

ACKNOWLEDGEMENTS

I'd like to take the time to quickly acknowledge those without whom I wouldn't have been able to put this book together.

Firstly, I'm grateful to Dr Travis Gee for his insights and feedback during the long haul that was the creation of Challenging the Black Dog. He has listened to my ramblings for over five years and provided extensive assistance and the provision of information on the psychological aspects of depression and its treatment from a professional point of view.

I'd like to thank Patmai DeVera for helping to bring my ideas onto paper with her illustrations. I'm beyond grateful that I stumbled upon her artwork over two years ago and that she was willing to work with me on this project. See more of her work at www.patmai.net.

I'd like to thank Patrick Knowles who patiently worked through numerous rounds of concepts (and what must have been annoyingly tiny tweaks) for the cover design while also providing valuable advice based on his many years in the field of design. See more of his work at www.patrickknowlesdesign.com.

I'd like to thank Paul Eyears for teaching me about the weird world of networking and helping to get some advance reader copies out to people I'd never have been able to reach otherwise.

A thank you to everyone-MH practitioners, consumers + advocates-who took the time to read through advance reader copies and send back comments, reviews and endorsements.

I'd also like to acknowledge the work of the countless people involved in developing the various types of therapies which have influenced the creation of this journal. Thee therapies include narrative therapy, dialectical behaviour therapy (DBT), art / creative therapy, music therapy, mindfulness-based cognitive therapy (MBCT), mindfulness-based stress reduction (MBSR) and cognitive behavioural therapy (CBT).

Last, but by no means least, are Simon and Mal, who gave me the final boost I needed to complete the journal to a stage and standard ready for release to the world.

;

This isn't the end.

Your story isn't over.

You are enough.

Hope is like the sun,
which casts the shadow
of our burden behind us.
-SAMUEL Smiles-

ABOUT VJ

VJ is a first-time author, introvert, and co-parent of a home-schooled teen.

She's spent over two decades dealing with depression, trichotillomania, social anxiety, disordered eating (EDNOS), and bipolar II. Fibromyalgia enjoys kicking her ass, so she's close friends with numerous hot water bottles.

She likes poking her dog while he's sleeping, comfy pants with pockets, silver bracelets, and making a mess with far too many DIY projects.

She dislikes (most) social media, having to wear makeup, photographs of herself, living with chronic pain, and watching her child grow up.

She lives on a small island off the coast of South East Queensland with an abundance of wildlife and far too many friendly mosquitos.

Her hair colours, like her medications, are subject to change.

NOTES FROM THE AUTHOR

Thank you for buying this book published by Offbeat Brains.

www.offbeatbrains.com

Reviews are gold to authors! If you've enjoyed using the journal, please consider rating it and reviewing it on Amazon and Goodreads.

To be among the first to hear about special offers, free content, and news about upcoming books and fun extras, sign up for n exclusive newsletter at offbeatbrains.com.

COMING IN 2019

Silencing the Inner Ghosts:
A Creative Outlet for Tackling Self-Harm

Finding the Healing Truth:
A Creative Outlet for Personal Discovery